THE DRAGON IN THE CASTLES

MYRDDIN AP DAFYDD

Adapted from Welsh by Gwyneth Owen

GWASG CARREG GWALCH

First published: 2019
© text: Myrddin ap Dafydd 2019
© illustrations: Chris Iliff 2019

ISBN: 978-1-84527-682-9

The publisher acknowledges the financial support
of the Welsh Books Council.

Cover and book design: Eleri Owen
Illustrations: Chris Iliff
Photos: Gwasg Carreg Gwalch, Croeso Cymru

Published by Gwasg Carreg Gwalch,
12 Iard yr Orsaf, Llanrwst, Dyffryn Conwy, Cymru LL26 0EH.
Tel: 01492 642031
e-mail: llyfrau@carreg-gwalch.cymru
website: www.carreg-gwalch.cymru

CONTENT

Welcome friend! Join us on our journey around the castles of Wales. We'll travel on the M4 motorway, and sometimes, on narrow country lanes, but this is really a journey through time. We'll go to the south, to the north and to mid Wales.

The most important character on the journey is Gran's Red Dragon. This old flag feels very different from our shiny red dragon flags of today. It's an old cloth banner, which Gran carried to Cardiff Arms Park on 13th March 1965. She waved it when Clive Rowlands was captain of Wales, and the national side beat Ireland 14:8 to win the Triple Crown and the Championship. Clive Rowlands was from Cwm Twrch, but Dewi Bebb, the winger from north Wales also scored the all-important second try.

Gran gave us – 11 year old twins, Gruff and Gwen – the old Red Dragon as a Christmas present. She'd kept it all these years and made it into a cushion for us.

Gran, who lives in Nantgaredig, said "Take it with you around Wales, and send us your photos and stories."

When Grandad, from Llanberis, saw the cushion he said, "What a good idea! Dewi Bebb's father – Ambrose Bebb – was a historian who called Wales 'Land of the Castles'. Did you know that there are more castles to the square mile here in Wales than in any other country in the whole world?"

Off we go then! We'll write the blog alternately – remember to follow both of us!

Followers 16

Gruff and Gwen
16 people are already following the Dragon in the Castles! and You!

Mam | Dad | Gran | Gramps | Grandma | Grandad | Angel | Bîns | Catrin | Draig | Gwcw | Gwil | Nerys | Tracs

The badge of the man at the paybooth at this castle on the banks of the river Wye, right on the border between Wales and England, said that his name was Dan.

"Hey! You can't take that into the castle!" he said, scowling and pointing at our Red Dragon cushion. "Don't you know the rules? No Welsh people allowed in the castle!"

For one second, we believed him. Then he grinned.

"Ha! Don't look so serious! Look through the window in the shop there – and you'll see a huge Red Dragon flying on the tower. The castle belongs to us, the Welsh, now. See this name: CADW. It means KEEP. That's the public body which looks after the castles, KEEPING them safe for visitors like you to enjoy and get to know their story. So, these days, everyone in the world is welcome to visit our castles, even the Welsh. But don't forget that this castle was originally built to keep the Welsh out."

Dan shows us pictures and maps in the exhibition.

"The Normans invaded the south of England in 1066, killing King Harold at the Battle of Hastings. All of England was defeated in a single afternoon. But then they came to Wales. In 1067 they crossed the river Wye – that fast, yellow river you can see below the castle – and set up camp on this clifftop. They'd captured this tract of Welsh land and were determined to keep hold of it. The Normans were like that. They started building this castle in that year – the first stone castle in Wales. It's been extended since then – a long snaking castle on the clifftop. It was the gateway to Wales for the Normans. Go and see the walls and towers and the old toilets teetering above the river like swallows'nests!"

Off we went. After climbing the Great Tower we could see the stone toilets on the wall ridges high above the cliff.

"Oh, I wouldn't like to wee in one of those!" screeched Gwen.

"Shush!" Mam whispered.

GATEHOUSE, DOOR AND DUNGEON

....

Chepstow, on the western bank of the river Wye was a gateway for the Romans (and, later, the Normans) to cross from the east to south Wales. The entrance to every castle is a weak point, so it's essential to guard it with a strong door defended by tall turrets. The 800 year old door can still be seen at Chepstow – the oldest surviving castle door in Europe.

A prison is often located near the gatehouse – a hole or pit which the Normans called *donjon*. Originally the *donjon* was the most secure tower in a castle, before the sturdy gatehouse was developed. Then the word came to mean the cells below the tower, or the cellar for prisoners. The worst cell was the one the Normans called the *oubliette* – 'the place to be forgotten'. Those unfortunate to be thrown in there never came out again.

"Why?" I asked.

"It says here," said Mam, reading from the castle's leaflet, "that Arthur's Cave can be found in the cliff below us."

"King Arthur's Cave?" Dad inquired.

"Yes. He and his army are sleeping inside, waiting for the call to wake up and lead Wales to freedom."

"They were asleep when the Normans built this castle then?" I asked.

When we returned to the shop, Dan asked, "Did you see the door?"

"That huge old door?" asked Dad.

"Yes," said Dan. "In 1190, that was the door of the gatehouse. It's the oldest castle door in Europe! That door kept out the Red Dragon. The Normans came into Wales through that door."

Followers 27

Gruff's mate Bîns
That door's brill!

Gwen's mate Nervous Nerys
The cell of the forgotten! What a dreadful idea!

Gran
I'm glad my Red Dragon went in through the gatehouse!

"What? We can enter this castle without paying?" asked Gruff, as we walked through a gap in the walls of Abergavenny castle.

"There's too little of it left to charge us an entrance fee," said Mam.

"It seems that Owain Glyndŵr and his army destroyed the place so thoroughly in 1404 that the Normans never returned here," said Dad. "It is said that a local woman got the gatehouse soldiers drunk before opening up to the Welsh."

"That was a sly trick," I muttered.

"Sly, you say?" To our surprise, a humpbacked old woman standing by the gap in the wall spoke to us. "This castle is full of sly things. Do you recognise one of these?"

She pointed to a narrow opening in the wall.

"An arrow slit?" asked Dad.

"Yes. And it's a cunning slit too. See how it's wider on this side to give the defenders more favourable angles? But these Normans were not very good bowmen. They used short bows or crossbows. The Welsh outside these walls were the experts."

"Didn't the Welsh use longbows?" asked Gruff.

"When the Normans arrived in their chain mail," said the old woman, "the Welsh realised they would need stronger bows to pierce their armour. They devised a six foot long bow which sent the arrows further and with greater force. The Welsh were the best bowmen in Europe at that time, and the archers of Gwent – this area – were the best in Wales."

"Wow!" I said. "We were better fighters than the Normans then?"

"Imagine the scene in April 1136," said the old woman in a low voice. "A squad of Normans cross those hills to steal more Welsh land. Suddenly the song of the birds is silenced in Cwm Grwyne Fawr as a shower of Welsh arrows, directed by Iorwerth ab Owain of Caerleon, kills all the invading Normans in a matter of minutes. Oh! The Normans were terrified of the Welsh archers. That's why

ARROW SLIT

Six years after the Welsh destroyed the castle at Abergavenny, Giraldus Cambrensis (Gerallt Gymro) wrote a travel book about Wales. He was shown the old gatehouse door at this castle. Even though it was made of stout oak 'the thickness of a man's palm' – some four inches/10cm thick – the Welsh arrow heads had pierced through the door and could still be seen protruding on the surface on the inner side.

The Welsh archers could kill an enemy from 150 meters. The Welsh longbow, which could even defeat an armed knight, was one of the main reasons why the Normans failed to conquer Wales. When armies across Europe saw what the Welsh could achieve with the longbow, they proceeded to copy them in the centuries that followed, thus transforming the history of battles across the continent.

William de Braose invited three hundred Welsh chieftains from Gwent to this castle on Christmas Day in 1175."

"The Normans invited the Welsh to their castle!" exclaimed Mam. "Fair play to them – that's true Christmas spirit."

"Hold on there," answered the old woman in a hoarse voice. "When the Welsh were seated at the tables feasting on meat and wine – without their weapons, naturally – de Braose stood up. 'Silence!' he roared. 'Since I am Lord of Gwent, I declare that every Welshman here must swear that he will never again carry a bow and arrows!' 'You have no right to ask this of us. You're just a murderer and a thief,' replied the Welsh. On a sign from de Braose, a multitude of armed Norman soldiers leapt from their hiding places and attacked the Welsh. Only one of them escaped to tell the horrific tale, and that was Iorwerth of Caerleon ..."

"Oh! I hate the Normans," cried Gruff.

"Was that the end of the Welsh in this area?" asked Mam.

"Seven years later the Welsh attacked the gatehouse and walls of this castle with their arrows. They were too strong for the Normans. When they returned over those hills, which form such a striking background to these valleys, the town and castle were smouldering ruins, and the High Sheriff and all the Normans were slain. Sniff these walls. They still reek of the smoke."

The four of us closed our eyes, and yes, we could smell the Welsh smoke of revenge on the dark walls!

When we turned to question the old woman further, there was no-one there ...

Followers 80

Gruff's mate Tracs
Yikes! That's a great story about the woman by the wall. I keep dreaming about her!

Gwen's mate Catrin
The worst Christmas story ever. Awful!

Gramps
Do you remember the bow I whittled for you when you were six, Gruff? I managed to cut my finger, and there was blood everywhere!

11

We're in the capital this March to watch Wales play Ireland! We've brought Gran's Red Dragon with us to encourage our national team. Before the game, we visit Cardiff castle.

Someone is selling Wales scarves near the entrance. How can we resist?!

"Do you play rugby then?" the man asked me.

"Yes, but I'm a bit small in my class."

"Tut," he replied. "Some of the world's best players have been small – many of them Welsh as well! Look at this huge wall and the strong gatehouse of this castle – once upon a time, a very small man defeated the Normans here at Cardiff."

Obviously, we were about to hear the story.

"In those days Wales was made up of many small countries. Each one had its own king or overlord, and here in Cardiff the leader was Ifor ap Meurig. His court was up the road in the hills where Castell Coch stands today. The Normans had built a mound here with a tower on top and a surrounding wall – you can see the tower through this entrance arch. The Norman baron was called William Fitz Robert. Ifor came to the castle to complain to William that another Norman baron was a complete nuisance, stealing Welsh land and property in the hills. He hoped William would see fair play, but do you know what William did?"

"No," replied Gwen. "Help him, perhaps?"

"Nothing of the sort! He threw Ifor into a cell at the base of the tower on the mound, and kept him there for several days."

"Was Ifor released later?" I asked.

"Yes. But he soon returned – in the dead of night this time, with half a dozen of his best soldiers. They left their horses in the shelter of trees down there by the river Taff – and how do you think they got into the castle?"

"Did they attack the guards at the entrance?" I suggested.

"Ah! Side-stepping the strongest defence is a better strategy sometimes," the bloke said, taking

MOTTE AND BAILEY CASTLE

....

When they invaded new lands, the Norman tactic was to build a small castle very quickly to defend their soldiers and establish a stronghold in an area where they were not welcome. They searched for a small hill, dug a moat around it, using the earth excavated to create a larger, steeper mound. Then they erected a stout wooden fence to enclose a patch of land for soldiers and animals to live. All the building materials would be available locally, and within ten days, their castle would be finished.

The Welsh used fire as their main weapon against these early castles. The wooden outer wall or palisade and the tower on the mound were quick to burn in a Welsh attack.

The Normans then built a stone castle on the mound, and surrounded the bailey with a stone wall. A drawbridge would link the tower to the flat land within the bailey.

Mote (mound) and *baile* (patch of land defended by a palisade or wall) are old French words.

payment for three mores scarves at the same time. "They had ropes, and since Ifor was a small, nimble fellow – known as Ifor Bach among his friends – he was over the wall in two ticks.

"Since he'd been in the Norman keep as a prisoner, he knew his way around. Like shadows, they tip-toed across the bailey, crept past the stables and storehouses, crossed the moat to the mound and climbed the tower stairs – right up to where William Fitz Robert and his wife slept!"

"The big bully in his castle!"

"Exactly! In no time, they had bound and gagged William, his wife and child. Before anyone realised what had happened they'd escaped out of the tower, across the bailey, over the wall and away up into the hills with their three hostages."

"Three – nil to the Welsh!" I laughed.

"The Normans searched everywhere for the baron and his family, but with no success. Ifor Bach had taken them to a cave in the hills well out of the enemy's way. Oh, he looked after them well enough, but reminded them that this is how the Welsh would be forced to live if the Normans continued to steal their land and homes. In the end, William promised to recognise the rights of the Welsh if he and his family could return to Cardiff castle. And so it was – they were released safely and returned to the castle. This time, William kept his word."

"Ifor Bach, a great Welshman," said Gwen.

"Indeed," said the scarf-seller. "Enjoy your castle visit – but remember that if you want to get something done – where there's a Will there's a way!"

Followers 124

Gwen's mate Draig
I've got a photo of the tower on the mound on my phone – and the flag flying there today is the Red Dragon of Wales!

Gruff's mate Gwcw
Wow! Ifor Bach can captain my team any time! But William Fitz Robert didn't play fair.

Grandad
I remember going to my first international rugby match in Cardiff when Barry John and Gerald Davies were playing. We're still small giants!

What a fantastic day! Gran and Gramps have brought us to Llandeilo for the afternoon. We're staying with them in Nantgaredig, and we're visiting the famous chocolate shop here in the town on the banks of the river Towy. We cross the great stone bridge, park the car and set off for the chocolate feast.

The four of us munch away and wander down the street to see 'Llandeilo Fawr' or *'Great Llandeilo'* church as it's called in the exhibition inside. This was Saint Teilo's main church, and we read that a valuable old parchment was created here in 730 called Saint Teilo's Book. A Saxon army stole it in the tenth century, and it's now known as the *Litchfield Gospels* as it's kept there in the English Midlands. Its great claim to fame is that it contains the earliest example of written Old Welsh.

"Llandeilo Fawr. The ancient church of Lord Rhys," booms a voice behind us.

We turn to see a bald man in grey monastic garb. He tells us the story.

"Dinefwr castle stands on that wooded rise above the valley. This was a Welsh castle, defending the lush Towy Valley where the best black cattle in the country were bred. Cattle were the most important possessions of the Welsh, and a strong king and powerful army were needed to protect them. That's exactly the sort of people Lord Rhys and the soldiers of Dinefwr were."

"But didn't invading armies from across the border come this far sometimes?" asked Gran.

"Yes," said the clerical gentleman. "They were never satisfied. Lord Rhys wanted peace and the chance for his people to live their quiet lives so, when King Henry II invited him to peace talks at Worcester, he gladly agreed. He was promised a safe passage. But do you know what Henry did, the pig?"

"No idea," said Gruff.

"He threw him into the castle dungeon! Then he sent a spy to the Towy valley to check out Lord Rhys' land. He wanted to find out whether it was worth invading the Welsh countryside. The spy ended up here at Llandeilo Fawr."

Y BWTRI (THE BUTTERY)

Bwtri is a word that has been used in Welsh for many centuries. People in north Wales and Ceredigion now use it for a pantry, a dairy or a storehouse for food and drink. In English, 'buttery' is used in the same way. However, like many words in the castle, the origin of the word is in the Old French of the Normans. The word *bouteilerie*, means the place to keep bottles. The *bwtri* would have been located between the main hall and the kitchen of the castles.

By the way, 'pantry' (food store) also comes from the old language of the castles. *Pain* is the French for bread, and a pantry is where *pain* is kept.

As we can see from this story about Dinefwr castle, the Normans were very interested in food and drink!

"The devil!" roared Gramps.

"Henry II's spy was met here at the church by a holy man called Gwyddan. 'Show me the court of Lord Rhys,' demanded the spy. 'I want to see how well you all live in this area' 'Follow me,' said Gwyddan."

Our monk beckoned us forward, and we soon realised that we were acting out the events of 1158. We are led from the town of Llandeilo up a narrow path through the woods. Soon the path began to climb, and then became very, very steep.

"Gosh!" said Gramps to Gran. "Hold on to my arm."

"On this spot, the spy asked Gwyddan if there was any drink available for a traveller. See that muddy puddle below that rock? Gwyddon knelt down and drank the water there, saying it was excellent at quenching a thirst! The Norman spy was amazed. 'Don't you have any wine?' he moaned."

"Gruff, have you any of that chocolate left?" I asked.

"Next, the Norman demanded food," said our guide. "So Gwyddan started eating leaves from the trees! 'What about a song to lighten the mood?' said the Norman and Gwyddan sang the saddest ballad he could think of. The sound was so mournful that a thick mist started forming under the trees."

"'I'm off home!' said the Norman. 'This is the most hellish place on earth!' And indeed, he persuaded Henry II to release Lord Rhys and to forget about attacking the Towy valley. You should have seen the feasting at Dinefwr castle when Rhys returned safely!"

Followers 188

Gwen's mate Angel
I love that holy man!

Gruff's mate Gwil
Rotters! They've been at it for hundreds of years! We have to win back Saint Teilo's Book!

Grandma
I've just been checking on the internet. There's a road wide enough to take a bus on the other side of the hill to reach Dinefwr castle. No need to climb the wooded crags after all!

"This gatehouse is huge – and so strong!" said Gwen walking between the round towers each side of the portcullis.

We're at Kidwelly castle today, on another holiday trip with Gran and Gramps from Nantgaredig. Once again, it's a short journey. They obviously live in an area where there was a great deal of excitement in the olden days.

"Have you brought the old Red Dragon, Gwen?" asked Gran.

"Of course!" Gwen opened her rucksack to show the cushion.

"Why don't we take a photo near the gatehouse to show how small the dragon is compared to these huge castles?"

"Blimey, the giant's gatehouse!" said Gramps. "How on earth did the Welsh think they could defeat the Normans and rid themselves of the rule of these powerful castles?"

Firstly, we climbed one of the gatehouse towers. We could see the sea from the very top.

I asked, "What's beyond that horizon, Gran?"

"Let me think," she said. "This is the river Gwendraeth in the valley below. To our right is Carmarthen Bay; that's the Gower Peninsula on the left and Devon and Cornwall over the horizon."

"I expect that ships from far away could reach Kidwelly castle in that case?" said Gwen.

A young girl in a green hoodie said, "The Normans were soldiers of the sea. I'm pleased to hear you bring the history to life! My name is Meinir and I work for CADW during the summer. I study history at Swansea University and lead guided tours round this castle."

"Interesting job, I should think," said Gramps.

"I meet people from all over the world," Meinir replied. "And yes, the Normans were pretty keen to rule the high seas. That's why they built castles on coastal estuaries – ships could

MURDER HOLES

· ·

These were open gaps high in the walls between supporting corbels on a projecting parapet. Soldiers defending the castle on the battlements could fling rocks, pour boiling oil or hurl burning torches through the murder holes on the heads of attackers at the foot of the walls or near the entrance.

The Normans called these *machicolations* – an old French word for 'severing the neck'.

bring in food, soldiers and weapons if the Welsh attacked them."

"Did the Welsh dare to attack this one?" I asked in amazement.

"Oh yes, several times," said Meinir. "But this was a difficult castle to overcome. See this gatehouse here? If the Welsh were threatening to attack, the soldiers would be ready for them. They'd lower the portcullis ..."

"What's a portcullis?" asked Gwen.

"In Old French, *port* – door and *coleice* – sliding," explained Meinir. "It's a heavy metal door which slides down from a great height to block the gatehouse entrance within seconds."

"So the Welsh couldn't get in?" said Gran.

"See these gaps here, by your feet? Murder holes! The Normans threw things at the attackers through those."

"No hopes then," muttered Gramps.

"The Welsh were defeated by the Normans of Kidwelly many times. Have you heard of Gwenllïan, the brave princess, who led a Welsh army against the Normans?"

"I've read about her!" said Gwen. "She

was killed, along with her sons, wasn't she?"

"That's right. It's a sad story," said Meinir. "That battle was fought up the valley, below Mynyddygarreg. The farm up there is still called Maes Gwenllïan."

"So this castle represents the might of the Normans?" I asked sadly.

"Don't you believe it!" said Meinir. "In 1225 Llywelyn Fawr (Llywelyn the Great) and his army came this way – and defeated the castles at Laugharne, Carmarthen, Llanstephan, Narberth, Cilgerran, Cardigan – and even this one, Kidwelly. The castle here was laid to ruin and burnt. The Normans were no match for the Welsh under Llywelyn the Great. Hey, I must dash – a group of Americans are waiting for me outside the entrance."

I shouted after her, "Don't forget to tell them about Llywelyn Fawr!"

Followers 225

Gwen's mate Nervous Nerys
Llywelyn Fawr went all the way from Gwynedd in the north to Kidwelly – and knocked out the Normans.

Gruff's mate Bîns
Crikey! The portcullis and the murder holes were really sly tricks!

Gramps
There's an eerie silence in Kidwelly today. I can almost hear Gwenllïan's cry and the triumphant shout of Llywelyn Fawr.

This morning we went to a bookshop on Cardigan High Street, to buy a quiz book about Wales.

"Oh! You're into quizzes, then?" asked the man behind the counter. "Here's a good question for you – 'Which Welsh castle did the Rebecca rioters attack?' Eh? Bet you can't answer that one!"

"But I thought the Rebecca rioters attacked tollbooths and wrecked tollgates," said Gruff.

"Yes, yes. But they destroyed one castle too! Which one do you think? Well this very one – Cardigan castle! In those days the remains of the Northern Gatehouse was on the High Street to the right of where this shop now stands. In 1843 it was destroyed by the rioters when they attacked the town. Yes, I'm telling you – it's important to have an upheaval from time to time! Did you know that the Welsh built their first siege engines to wreck castles here in Ceredigion?"

"Engines to wreck castles. Wow – they sound like fun!" said Gruff.

"You see, the Welsh were fed-up with the cheek of the Normans, marching their armies up and down the land, and building castles everywhere. The Welsh had been able to burn the early castles, but they needed a new plan when the Normans started building castles of stone. By the 12th century, Wales had two strong leaders – Owain Gwynedd in the north and Lord Rhys in the south. They made the Normans flee and stole their castles, using them to defend their lands against the enemy's armies. They learnt from the Normans themselves how to attack castles and how to defend them. When Lord Rhys and his brothers captured Llanstephan castle the Normans tried to win it back by placing long ladders against the walls. But the Welsh pushed the ladders away so that the Normans landed in the moat!"

"Good job!" said Gruff.

"And it was here at Ystrad Meurig, Ceredigion that the Welsh first used sling and catapult

A CHAIR AT THE LORD'S TABLE

....

The castle's main hall would be in the most secure part of the castle – the main tower or the inner keep, as a rule. This was an important room both militarily and politically. At the upper end of the main hall – closest to the lord's private quarters – a grand table and the lord's chair would be set on a dais. Here the lord would stage the court meetings and also celebrate feasts to mark holidays or battle victories. His main courtiers would surround him at the grand table.

When Lord Rhys held his Eisteddfod at Christmas 1176, the main prize for the best bard and the best harpist was a chair at the Lord's table. Other generous prizes were awarded to the performers – but the chief honour went to the winners of the chairs. The Harpist's Chair was won by a young man from the Cardigan court, and a poet from Gwynedd won the Bard's Chair. This is the oldest record of an Eisteddfod, and the tradition of awarding a chair to winning bards has been maintained in Wales since that time.

engines to breach the castle walls and defeat the Normans. Look, go down to see Cardigan castle by the river. When Lord Rhys managed to expel the Normans from their earth and wooden castle in 1171, he moved his main court to Cardigan and started building a stone castle here. There's a man with foresight – he wasn't going to give up this prime site easily. This was the first castle built by the Welsh. It took them five years to complete the work, and it has taken years again in this century to restore the castle and welcome visitors. Do go and see it – it's well worth a visit. And return here afterwards with the answer to this question. Lord Rhys celebrated the building of the castle by holding an Eisteddfod inside at Christmas 1176. This is the first Eisteddfod mentioned in the history of Wales. He sent messengers throughout the land to declare that there were to be competitions and special prizes for poets and musicians. What were the main prizes, then? Eh? That's your question! You'll find the answer in the castle!"

Followers 286

Gwen's mate Catrin
'Castle-wrecking engines' – didn't they have fun in those days?

Gruff's mate Tracs
The Normans came as far as Cardigan? Well, some people have a nerve!

Grandma
Hey you two. Remember the chair at next year's school eisteddfod. It would be great to see one of you two winning it!

"Excuse me! Can you come in as quickly as you can and make your way to the far side of the castle please?"

The family have just arrived at Cricieth castle, and after climbing up the path to the main gate, a girl, dressed in black, wearing sunglasses and headphones, and carrying a backpack and a mobile phone approached them with a list of instructions.

"We're in the middle of recording a short film to welcome visitors," she said.

From the foot of the castle's furthest wall, the family watch the famous presenter walk through the gateway, looking around him dramatically before focusing on the camera and beginning his story:

"Llywelyn Fawr was born around 1173 and by 1202 he was a strong, successful leader ruling most of north Wales. He would become the chief among Welsh princes, by the end of his life, building many stone castles to defend his lands against the Normans – Dolbadarn, Ewloe, Castell y Bere, Carn Dochan and here at Cricieth, on a rounded hill above the sea cliffs."

"So, Llywelyn was a great builder, then?" I said.

"Shhh by those walls there, please!" shouted the girl with the headphones.

"Watch out, Gruff, or she'll throw you into a cellar underneath that tower!" said Gwen.

"I said Shhh!"

The presenter walks towards the round tower which is to the left of the entrance, looking from inside the castle.

"This tower is called the 'Engine Tower'. Some castles were adapted to construct a special platform on the high walls of the tower for a defending machine. The Welsh had to learn quickly how to defend themselves from Norman trebuchets, ballistas, mangonels and perriers. Yes, quite a mouthful – but these were the French machines a fierce army outside

TREBUCHET

··

This was a wooden machine which hurled huge rocks and all kinds of missiles at a castle's defences during a siege. It was a French invention brought to England in the 13th century by the Normans.

Trebuchet   from old French: 'to hurl over …' This was an engine to hurl missiles over walls to create chaos within.

Two new ones of these have been recreated and placed outside the walls of Caerphilly castle in 2018. Other siege engines existed.

Ballista   a giant crossbow which could fire a huge arrow or spear capable of wounding several soldiers in one go. The word 'ballistic' comes from this word!

Mangonel   a hurling engine to fling smaller rocks or fire bombs.

Perrier   a long hurling arm to fling shot which also derives from the old French word for large stone: *perron*.

would use to try and seize this castle from Llywelyn Fawr."

The presenter now walks to the centre of the open grassy triangle inside the castle walls.

"Imagine standing here, with these engines hurling all sorts of things over the walls at you. Not just rocks and fire bombs – but dead, infected cattle, in order to spread disease among the castle inhabitants, or loose quicklime which would blind them."

He walks back towards the gatehouse and looks up at the stones above.

"But this castle was eventually destroyed in 1404 by Owain Glyndŵr and his army. They say that burn marks can still be seen on the gatehouse stones."

"Hurrah!" Gwen shouted.

"Shhh!" whispered the girl with the headphones.

The presenter continued.

"Of course, what remains today is this amazing view of the mountains from Snowdon down to Cadair Idris. These mountains were the best defensive castle for the Welsh, and they still stand guard over the sea to the west."

Followers 310

Gwen's mate Gwcw
Great vision, Llywelyn Fawr!
I love the setting!

Gruff's mate Draig
Diseased cattle and quicklime! Ugh!

Gran
Would you like to work in the media, Gruff and Gwen? Great opportunity to meet interesting kids, I'm sure.

Us twins have just celebrated our birthday, and one of the best presents ever were vouchers for the Zip Wire at Llechwedd quarry, Blaenau Ffestiniog – or 'the thrill thread' as Mam called it. What amazing views!

After the excitement, the car has climbed over the pass and we've stopped for a few moments to enjoy that particular view.

"There's Yr Wyddfa (*Snowdon*)," said Dad, "and Crib Goch like a hedgehog's back, prickly, jagged and dangerous."

"That rounded peak ahead is Moel Siabod," said Mam. "Do you remember, we climbed it from Capel Curig?"

"Is that the same mountain?" I asked in amazement. "Gosh, it's big."

"Some of the hill shepherds around here say it's the most extensive mountain in Europe, rising from a very broad base to just one summit," said Dad.

"Wow! This place is full of mountains and crags," said Gruff. "Only one or two white-washed farmhouses to show that people live here."

"There's one other special building," said Dad. "Can you spot it? Below the pass there, on a rise at the foot of Moel Siabod. Can you see a stone tower down there?"

We follow the direction of Dad's finger and search the mountain pastures and crags of this wild landscape. "Oh! I see it!" shouted Gruff. "A dark, square tower."

"Yes, the old castle belonging to the Welsh," said Mam. "Dolwyddelan castle. It looks like part of the mountain itself, don't you think?"

"That's true in a sense," said Dad. "These mountains were the stronghold of the Welsh princes. With their backs to these crags, fighting the armies of the English king, they were like a rugby team playing at home. They never gave up. They had routes crossing these mountain passes, linking all their castles. If the Normans ruled the seas, it was the Welsh who ruled the mountains."

We then go down the valley to see the castle properly.

There's plenty of parking space nearby and we walk to the farmhouse to buy tickets for the castle.

"Cross the farmyard," said the farmer's wife. "And if you see a young lad rushing about trying to finish his chores, that'll be my son, Ieuan. Tell him his mam says that it's time he came into the house – he's got an important rugby match this afternoon, and he must line his stomach beforehand."

KEEP

The 'keep' is the largest and most important tower, and the best defended in the castle. Sometimes it is on a mound within the inner walls – as in Cardiff castle, or forms part of the inner walls, but built taller and stronger than the other towers.

There are two Welsh castles from the days of Llywelyn Fawr in the mountains of Eryri – at Dolwyddelan and Dolbadarn. Little remains of the original castles today, except both keeps, withstanding stormy weather and appearing as permanent as the surrounding crags.

The obvious difference between them is that the keep at Dolwyddelan is square whilst the keep at Dolbadarn castle is round. Dolwyddelan castle was built around 1210-40, with two storeys in the original keep. Dolbadarn castle was built in the 1230s with three storeys to the keep.

Yes, the keep was a safe place. The princes kept their most important prisoners in the keep at Dolbadarn. Lord Grey of Ruthin, the Norman baron who was a thorn in Owain Glyndŵr's side, was imprisoned there. He was captured after the battle of Ruthin in 1402 and held captive at Dolbadarn until the king agreed to pay a huge ransom to secure his release.

From the pass, Dolwyddelan castle had looked tiny in the shadow of the Eryri mountains (*Snowdonia*). But it looks huge and strong from down here.

"Is it true that Llywelyn Fawr was born here?" asked Dad.

"Well, there's a strong tradition that he was born at Dolwyddelan," said the woman. "But it was probably at a wooden castle further down towards the village. He was obviously very fond of the place, because he built this stone castle here. He loved the Conwy valley. He had a hunting lodge at Trefriw and he founded a church there for his wife Siwan – to save her the uphill climb to the old church at Llanrhychwyn. In his last days Llywelyn retreated to the abbey at Aberconwy where Conwy castle stands today. His stone coffin can be seen in a side chapel at Llanrwst church to this day."

"I've got to go, Mam!" A wild-looking boy pushes past us with his rugby kit over his shoulder and a bacon butty in his mouth.

"Good luck! Hope you win!" his mother called after him.

"Of course, we will. We're playing at home today," Ieuan replied.

Followers 363

Gruff's mate Gwil
Quarry zip wires and home games in the mountains – that's the way to make heroes!

Gwen's mate Angel
Eating and running at the same time and talking with his mouth full – tut tut!

Grandad
The Normans destroyed the old Welsh abbey at Aberconwy to build their castle on its site – I wonder how many of Wales' historic buildings have been lost over the centuries?

We've come to Carmarthenshire for a holiday during the half-term, and today we're visiting another castle. Great! The girl on the path ahead of us paused to look through her binoculars. The turrets and walls of Carreg Cennen castle rose proudly in front of us above the cliff. But the girl wasn't staring at the castle. Her binoculars were trained on the skies above. We soon caught up with her.

"Can you see it?" she asked.

"The castle?" asked Gwen. "Yes, it's big and strong, isn't it?"

"No, high up above the castle," she replied. "A red kite!"

We all follow the angle of the binoculars up to the clouds.

"There!" shouted Gwen. "I can clearly see the forked tail!"

"Look at the sun on those feathers," said Mam. "Oh, you could swear that it's a bird made of copper shining there above us."

"And hovering there so still and so high!" exclaimed Dad.

"The whole history of Wales is represented by that bird's story," said the girl. "It was hunted and hunted until, at one time, only one female bird and one nest remained. But that nest was the bird's castle, and from the strength of that one nest the bird recovered to spread its wings over most of the land."

"Are you a castle lady or a bird lady?" asked Dad.

"Both!" she replied. "Birds are my great interest, but as the kite's story makes clear, you cannot have birds without habitat. The same is true of castles – they too have their habitat or terrain."

"Carreg Cennen has a very rough terrain in any case!" said Gwen. "If I was an enemy, I wouldn't have the energy to fight by the time I'd reached the base of those towers!"

SECRET TUNNEL

....

Many castles have romantic stories about secret tunnels. According to tradition in Llanberis, a secret tunnel leads from Dolbadarn castle to the shores of Llyn Peris. Of course, no one has ever discovered this tunnel. 'It's possible that the roof has collapsed and that it's been closed for centuries. But yes, there once was a tunnel ...'

Of course it's true that a secret tunnel was one way of defeating a besieging army which hoped to capture the leader or starve out the regiment. People could escape through a secret tunnel, or supplies could be brought in by the same route.

In Carreg Cennen castle, however, there is a vaulted passage which leads to a natural cave. This 'secret tunnel', part of the castle's defences, has the imagination racing.

"Yes, it's a splendid location," said the girl. "It's like a high nest on the crag, with the wild mountain beyond. This was a Welsh castle, and it challenges us from that craggy top with a stubborn authority."

As we near the castle, the sun rebounds from the stones so that they appear to shine.

"The rock on this rise is limestone," Dad explained. "Naturally, local stones were used to build the castle. Since that stone is white, the castle is visible and striking from a distance, wouldn't you agree?"

Soon we're wandering around the castle imagining the excitement here when Lord Rhys arrived, or Llywelyn ap Gruffudd on one of his raids from the north. Even after the Welsh armies had been defeated, Carreg Cennen remained on the list of spoils in times of rebellion. In 1287, Rhys ap Maredudd rebelled against Edward I and captured Carreg Cennen, before attacking Dryslwyn castle the same afternoon. During Owain Glyndŵr's rebellion, his army came over the mountains and laid siege to the castle, forcing the Normans to yield in the long term. Yes, there's a strong feeling here that we Welsh own the place – and even if things sometimes go against us, there's plenty of time left to return and occupy the place once more.

As we leave, the red kite is still above us, its cry echoing through the land and the sun shining on its red feathers.

Followers 412

Gruff's mate Bîns
The red kite – that's the bird for Wales if ever there was one. Hang on in there, you amazing bird!

Gwen's mate Nervous Nerys
A tunnel! Just the place to breed bats?

Gran
I'm looking at a calendar on our wall – a coloured photo of Carreg Cennen castle is this month's picture. But a photo doesn't really do justice to the castle!

Today we're in the Severn Valley and have climbed up to Llywelyn's castle at Dolforwyn. A group of schoolchildren from Newtown are ahead of us and they are led by the current 'Bardd Plant Cymru' – the Welsh Children's Poet. We listen in on the workshop.

"Sometimes, two castles close together look like a pair of rugby posts, or two goals on a football field. This one belongs to one team, that one to another," says the Poet.

"They face each other across the valley, and you can almost hear them roaring and shouting at each other! On this side of the Severn valley you have Dolforwyn, Llywelyn ap Gruffudd's castle. On the other side, closer to England there is the Norman castle at Montgomery. Two goals facing each other. Or what else could they be?"

A hand shoots up from the group of children.

"Two dogs barking at each other," says the boy.

"Oh, very good." The Poet is obviously delighted with this response.

"Two bulls in one field, lowering their horns, ready for a fight," a girl adds.

"Brilliant! Any more suggestions?"

"Two sumo wrestlers!"

"There we have some dramatic descriptions of these two castles," says the Poet. "Right, follow me out of the gatehouse to see where the old Welsh town stood just below Dolforwyn castle. Did you know that Llywelyn hoped to make this town the capital of Wales?"

The group move on and Gruff is amazed. "The capital of Wales! On this ridge? Did you know that, Mam?"

"Let's read the heritage noticeboards around the site to learn the real story."

As we read the noticeboards, the pieces fall into place. The river Severn is the longest in

England and Wales. From its source on Pumlumon it flows eastwards through Newtown and Welshpool, over the border into England before flowing southward, reaching the Welsh/English border near Chepstow. It's a pleasant broad valley even before leaving Wales. But, unfortunately, it leads eastwards, creating a gap in the hills and mountains that defend Wales from armies from the east.

"This valley was the gap which allowed the enemy into Wales, then?" says Gruff.

"What a pity the Severn doesn't flow the other way!" I thought.

"This is the way the Romans, the Saxons and the Normans came to mid Wales," explained Dad.

"And of course they had their castles," says Mam. "It says here that the Normans had started to build a strong stone castle in Montgomery by 1230 and in 1267, they were building a wall to defend the town as well."

"Llywelyn ap Gruffudd was at his most powerful at that time," reads Dad. "So he started building a castle at Dolforwyn in 1273 and established a market town to stop the Normans pushing further along the Severn valley."

"Just think if the plan had worked," says Gruff dreamingly. "We'd have good motorways linking Cardiff, Caernarfon, St David's and Wrexham – and they'd all meet here!"

BUROUGH

....

It's one thing to build a castle, another to pay for it and meet the yearly costs of keeping and maintaining it.

The main purpose of a castle is to create a safe place for an army trying to control a piece of land. The soldiers do not work, except for preparing for battle and practising their fighting skills. The castle will need a cobbler, tailors, a blacksmith, stable boys, a baker, cooks, a butcher, a beekeeper, a fisherman, a brewer, a musician and a bard, as well as other types of shopkeepers and craftsmen to fulfil the soldiers' needs. In other words the castle needs a market town to feed and entertain the soldiers.

When he builds a castle, the king or lord builds a town in its shadow with an outer wall to defend the town. The townspeople have a ready market and good prices for their goods – they get special 'market rights'. They have to pay the king for the right to be part of the castle's town. Someone living within the walls was called a 'burgess' – paying a yearly rent for a house, a workshop and a garden. Several 'burgesses' together near a castle will form a 'borough' – a town whose inhabitants enjoy special privileges and who are defended by the castle, the army and the king.

As we meet the Poet and the schoolchildren near the gatehouse, we're discussing the possible site for a National Airport.

"When Edward I attacked this castle and destroyed parts of it," says the children's Poet, "he forbade Llywelyn from rebuilding the walls. 'You can not close the Hole in the Wall' said Edward. Why don't we write a poem about 'The Hole in the Wall'?"

Followers 465

Gruff's mate Tracs
A capital city in mid Wales? We could watch a game at the National Stadium every week in that case!

Gwen's mate Catrin
But we wouldn't be able to stay at the Urdd's centre in Cardiff Bay if the capital was up here!

Gramps
The Welsh have only recently repaired their holes in the walls at Dolforwyn, making it possible for us to visit the castle ruins. I recall the opening ceremony by CADW in 2009 when they'd completed the excavations on the site.

It's Saturday during the Llangollen International Eisteddfod week, and today we've found a great spot on Bridge Street to watch the parade of singers, instrumentalists and dancers from various countries. They're all in colourful traditional dress, waving flags and making friends!

"Coming together in joy and peace," said Mam. "That was the reason the Welsh people of Llangollen organised this International Eisteddfod at the end of the Second World War."

"You're speaking Welsh! How lovely," said a girl standing next to us. "I come from Japan. My name is Aiko. I've been learning Welsh on Skype because I love Welsh music."

"Oh! Well done!" said Dad.

"Excuse me. How do you get to that castle over there?" Aiko then asked, pointing to the impressive ruin on the hilltop beyond the bridge.

"There's a path up that rise the other side of the bridge," said Dad.

"Is it far?" asked Aiko.

"No, about 45 minutes, maybe," answered Dad.

"And what is it called?" asked Aiko.

"Dinas Brân," said Mam. The Japanese girl then asked, "Is there a good view from the castle there?"

"We've never been up there!" replied Gwen.

"Hey!" said Mam. "It's a fine day. We have a couple of hours to spare. Why don't we visit Dinas Brân castle with Aiko?"

Fifteen minutes later we've crossed the bridge over the river Dêe and are following the signs up the hill on one side of the valley.

"You don't have to tell us, here's another Welsh castle," said Gwen. "There's a steep climb up to each of them!"

DITCH

The favourite defences of the Welsh were castles built on high cliffs – the steep slopes formed part of the defences. The pattern of the outer walls would also follow the jagged peak, creating interesting forms that were difficult to access.

Dinas Brân castle is noted for the deep ditch carved out of the rocks surrounding the walls – making it very difficult to reach the castle. Of course – it also served as a quarry providing a convenient source of building stone for the castle.

Ditches are an essential element of the defence of Norman castles too – often their ditches were filled with water with a drawbridge above to reach the gatehouse.

A ditch around a castle is called a 'moat', which comes from the same Norman word as mote – the castle mound. The Normans created a mote by digging a ditch, creating a mound of soil and gravel in the centre.

"This one is older than the Welsh Princes," said Dad. "The Celts had a hillfort on this rise. You know, earth walls and ditches surrounding the summit with a village of round huts within."

"Oh! It's so steep!" said Aiko, with a smile. "And since the Celts were fond of legends, you can be sure there are plenty of stories about the place," said Mam. "Have you heard about the giant, Bendigeidfran, Aiko? He's the 'Brân' in the name of the place, and there are also stories about King Arthur and about fairies linked to the castle."

"It still looks like a fairy tale castle!" said Aiko.

"When one of the Normans came here," explained Mam, "he sent word to the king that this was the strongest, safest castle in Wales – and in England too, if it came to that."

"And yet, the Normans took over here!" I said, amazed.

"Oh no," said Dad. "Gruffudd ap Madog, prince of Powys, built this castle around 1260. By 1276, Edward's huge armies were pressing upon the borderland in this area. The Welsh decided to burn the castle rather than let it become a Norman stronghold."

We've now reached the summit. A deep ditch has been dug out of the hard rock surrounding the ruins.

"Here we are," said Dad. "The Welsh cut into the rock to form a ditch and used the stones to build the castle."

"Good idea!" said Aiko. "Better than dragging the stones up that hill. But just look at that view ..."

Followers 523

Gruff's mate Draig
A girl from Japan speaking Welsh! Great!

Gwen's mate Gwcw
All this talk of climbing steep slopes up to castles makes me very thirsty.

Grandma
Grandad and I remember being on the bridge at Llangollen during the Eisteddfod many years ago – a very romantic spot!

"Don't you think that a Norman castle looks like a big round cheese?" asked Dad this morning.

"Cheese?" said Gruff. "I can see that a Welsh castle looks like a mountainous messy meringue with a strawberry on top – but why cheese?"

"Think about it," said Dad. "Norman castles are built on level ground – quite different from the clifftop Welsh castles. They liked having plenty of room to create an oval shape around the keep and courtyards, then the moat, and then the outer walls – the whole thing like a big cheese. The next town we're visiting is also well known for cheese – Caerphilly cheese."

"Caerphilly – that's Gramps' favourite cheese," said Mam.

"And what do we have in Caerphilly?" asked Gruff. "Another castle which looks like cheese?"

"More than that," replied Dad. "It's the end of July – the Big Cheese Festival is on. Funfair, performances, food festival, music . . ."

"And the Big Cheese Race!" said Mam.

We walk around a vast network of lakes and ditches before arriving at the drawbridge and gatehouse. "This is absolutely huge!" said Gruff.

"It's the largest castle in Wales," explained Dad. "And one of the largest in Europe. It was built by a Norman called Gilbert de Clare in 1268 because he was afraid of the influence of Llywelyn ap Gruffudd. By that date, Llywelyn had united all of Wales apart from a few tracts of land still in the hands of greedy Normans like de Clare. Llywelyn had been proclaimed Prince of Wales, with almost every Welsh leader, and even the English crown, recognising him as the chief authority in the land. His armies had destroyed the Norman strongholds and he had regained much of the land the Welsh had lost to the Norman lords in the borderlands. In 1270, Llywelyn came to Caerphilly and destroyed the castle which was in the process of being built."

BARBICAN

··

The 'barbican' is an additional structure in the outer walls to defend a town or castle. Once more, this word came to Wales with the Normans, but it comes originally from Arabic.

The Normans took many of their ideas about castle building from the Crusades. These were horrific wars in the Middle East when some of the kings in Europe joined forces to create a 'Christian' army to regain Jerusalem from the Arabs or the 'Moors' as they were known in those days.

Sometimes the barbican may be no more than a triangular stone wall to defend the lower wall against being penetrated. At other times it will be a tall structure in front of, or above the gatehouse, providing a good platform for shooting arrows or throwing missiles at attackers. At Caerphilly, a series of extra towers in the outer wall jut out of the wall, making things difficult for the enemy outside.

"Yet the Normans obviously liked this spot?" said Gruff. "They came back later?"

"Yes – and built this castle, strengthening it from year to year," said Mam. "You can feel the fear of another united Welsh uprising here. That fear makes the walls quake!"

"Is that why that tower is crooked, looking as if it's about to fall?"

"Yes, one of the towers at Caerphilly castle leans even more than the famous tower at Pisa! The south-eastern tower leans 10° from the vertical – as a result of damage caused by Oliver Cromwell's army apparently. Now, a wooden sculpture of a man helps to prevent the tower from falling.

"Even though this was a strong castle," said Dad, "that didn't stop the Welsh from trying to capture it. In 1316, Llywelyn Bren – one of Ifor Bach's descendants – led a Welsh revolt by laying siege to Caerphilly and attacking many Norman castles in Glamorgan. When things turned out badly for him, he gave himself up to the Normans, claiming that it was better that one man be punished rather than a whole nation being destroyed."

"What happened to Llywelyn Bren?" asked Gruff.

"He was killed in a most barbaric way in Cardiff in 1318," said Dad.

"They're still talking about erecting a memorial to Llywelyn Bren," said Mam.

Followers 613

Gwen's mate Angel
A funfair in a castle! Sounds good!

Gruff's mate Gwil
In killing Llywelyn Bren they killed a hero!

Gramps
Don't forget to bring some Caerphilly cheese home with you!

We've just returned from the school's history trip – a bus load of us went to north-east Wales. Our teacher, Mrs Morgan, gave us some information.

"At the moment, you're learning about Wales' first War of Independence, which is why we're visiting the places on this trip. By the Treaty of Montgomery in 1267, Wales was a new unified country within Europe, with Prince Llywelyn its strong leader. Firstly, we'll visit Llywelyn's castle at Ewloe – one of the Welsh castles in the north-east. This is known as 'the castle in the wood', fortified by Llywelyn to defend the land reclaimed from the Normans by the Welsh."

Ewloe castle is an amazing place, close to the border on the road to Chester. You have to cross a field to reach it. At first, there's no sign of the castle, then – you see it in a wooded hollow still looking strong and defiant. From Ewloe, we head for the coast.

"Edward I was proclaimed king of England in 1272," said Mrs Morgan. "Edward was a cruel, unforgiving brute – even towards his own family. He was also very ambitious. He hero-worshipped King Arthur, and wanted to be head of all of Britain – exactly as Arthur had defeated the Saxons in the 6th century. He led huge armies against Scotland during his reign, but, before that, he had turned his attention on Wales.

"Edward must have studied his family history. He learnt from the mistakes he made in 1263 and those of his father, Henry III, in 1257. Earlier kings too had brought huge armies to north Wales without defeating the Welsh. How did the Welsh fight?"

"Quick attacks!" said Gwcw.

"Using woods and cliffs," said Angel.

"Well done," said Mrs Morgan. "The Welsh were guerrilla fighters, taking advantage of the lie of the land, and a large, slow army with lots of equipment and wagons had no chance against them. In 1277 Edward came from Chester to north east Wales along the flat land

BASTIDE

···

Bastide is the name for a town or village defended by fortified walls – again a name from old French, and still used in Provence in south-east France for the fortress villages found on hilltops in the area.

The first Norman bastide in Wales was the one built in 1277 at Flint. It was a town for English immigrants. From above, the pattern of Flint's streets still reflects the grid pattern of the original fortress town. The town and castle were built in a spot where no settlement existed beforehand – an 'empty' tract of land was chosen for this ambitious build. The town and castle share the defences. This was the pattern for other Norman towns built in the shadow of a castle in later years – for example, Aberystwyth, Caernarfon and Conwy.

The town was burnt down by the Welsh in 1282, 1294 and by Owain Glyndŵr in 1400.

near this coast. He built a good road, clearing many trees from Chester to Deganwy, using ships to carry arms and equipment by sea. Without trees to shelter them, Llywelyn's army had no cover from which to attack the invaders."

The bus has reached the car park at Flint castle by this time. The river Dee marshes and the sea are ahead of us, with the large round towers of the castle rising above the defensive walls and ditches. Before long we are by the large keep.

"The walls of this tower are 23 feet thick!" said Mrs Morgan. "It's a castle within a castle, very like other large towers in France. Mr James of St George – a Frenchman – was the chief architect of Edward's castles. Edward started building the castle in 1277 while fighting against Llywelyn. He brought workers from England here – 970 labourers, 300 carpenters, 300 woodsmen, 200 stone masons and 12 blacksmiths. The project cost him £7,000 – over £3 million in our money. Edward was an ambitious king. He wasn't afraid of spending money."

We're all quiet as we walk round the huge towers. They look like a massive drum set. By listening carefully, the heavy thump, thump of the drumbeat can still be heard today.

Followers 745

Gruff's mate Bîns
It's amazing that the Welsh dared to attack such a stronghold so many times. Good for them!

Gwen's mate Nervous Nerys
Edward sounds like a powerful great bully.

Grandad
I know a song about an old donkey who died while carrying coal to Flint. I wonder if he was related to Edward?

The bus took us from Flint to the castle at Rhuddlan.

"This is the last castle we'll visit today," said Mrs Morgan. "You can wander about by yourselves. You know what features to look out for by now. Note the strength of the walls and towers and don't forget to go down to the solitary tower by the river to see the remains of the quay."

"Come on, Gruff," said Gwcw, going through the main gate between the two large towers.

"Hey, look," said Gruff when they reached the inner courtyard. "There are two identical towers and a gatehouse in the furthest corner directly opposite this gatehouse."

"The castle is perfectly square, with each pattern repeated," said Gwcw. "It looks just like a board for playing Ludo!"

Half an hour later, Mrs Morgan called us back to the middle of the courtyard.

"This was Edward's first base in Wales," she explained. "Unlike other kings from London, he didn't have to escape back to English castles when winter set in. He stayed safely and cosily inside this fortress. With a town established around the castle he was in a strong position."

"But Llywelyn was still at large?" I asked.

"Yes, of course," said Mrs Morgan. "The high mountains on the other side of the river Conwy formed a natural fortress for the Welsh. Edward didn't dare venture that far. But he still eyed the whole of Wales, plotting and creating rifts between Llywelyn and other Welsh leaders. He also started using English law in Wales."

"Getting rid of the old Welsh laws – the Laws of Hywel Dda?" said Gruff.

"Yes. This made the Welsh very angry and in 1282, the Second War of Welsh Independence started. Dafydd, Llywelyn's brother, attacked Hawarden castle and took it from the Normans. Edward led a large army along the north Wales coast, but it was thoroughly beaten as it tried to cross from Anglesey to the mainland in the battle of Moel-y-don. Llywelyn went to mid Wales to

QUAY

....

Whenever possible, Edward used local wood and stone to build his castles. If more stone, lime or gravel was needed, it was brought by ship from quarries near Chester and the Wirral.

In wartime, quick access by sea was important as part of the castle's defence, and that of the garrisons inside. As a result, most of the 14 new castles Edward built in north Wales are on the coast, and a quay or harbour form a vital part of the plan.

Rhuddlan is a castle on the banks of the river Clwyd. It's an important location, dominating a ford across the river – but what about help from ships? Edward's architects built a huge canal from the sea right up to the castle walls. 66 workmen spent 3 years working 6 days a week on its construction. That shows how important the support of ships was to Edward's castles. Rhuddlan castle has four gatehouses, and one of the most important is the Watergate next to the quay.

drum up more support, but he was unexpectedly killed in a sudden attack at Cilmeri on the banks of the river Irfon in December 1282. When his Norman attacker realised who his victim was, he cut off his head and brought it here to Rhuddlan to show Edward."

"Llywelyn's head!" exclaimed Gwcw. "The Prince of Wales' head was carried into this castle?"

"Yes," said Mrs Morgan. "And then it was taken across the Severn and all the way to London to be displayed at the Tower. In October 1283, Llywelyn's brother, Dafydd, was brought here as a prisoner. He was then taken to Shrewsbury to be dragged through the streets, tied behind horses. They hanged him but kept him alive while his entrails were cut from his body and burned. His body was quartered with the four parts sent to different English cities, but his head was taken to the Tower of London to be displayed next to his brother's."

"Ugh! The walls of this castle are stained red with Welsh blood," said Gruff.

"In 1284, Edward enacted a law in this town – known as the Statute of Rhuddlan. Llywelyn's principality now belonged to the king, and was divided into three counties in the north – Anglesey, Caernarfon and Meirioneth – and two in the south – Cardigan and Carmarthen. He then appointed officers to rule Wales on his behalf – magistrates, sheriffs and bailiffs."

"Wales must have suffered immensely in the 1280s under Edward's administration," said Gruff.

Followers 813

Gwen's mate Catrin
Playing Ludo in a castle – that sounds like a good game.

Gruff's mate Tracs
Edward's castles were castles of blood.

Gran
I remember reading about a parchment which recorded 'the king's gift' in Edward's castles – he rewarded his soldiers with money for every Welshman's head that was brought back to the castle.

"Healthy local honey! Conwy honey!" A stallholder shouts across the square. It's the 13th of September and we've been to Conwy's Honey Fair.

"This ancient fair dates back to the age of the castle," said Mam. "The king gave the towns with castles a special charter – giving the citizens the right to hold certain markets and fairs. Conway Seed Fair is still held on 26th of March every year, and the Honey Fair on today's date."

"Looking for honey?" asked the stallholder. "This is wildflower honey from the Conwy valley. The best you can buy!"

"I didn't realise there were so many honey producers in this area," said Dad looking across the square and down the main street."

"There are about 25 stallholders here today," said the beekeeper, "each selling his product. It's been a sunny summer, so the beehives are full of honey."

"And you've had the right to sell honey at this fair since the days of Edward I?" said Mam.

"Well, not me personally!" replied the beekeeper. "I'm not quite that old! And, of course, as a Welshman – I would not have been given land to keep bees within the town walls, nor the right to live here or trade at the fair."

"How did the local Welsh people live then?" asked Gwen.

"They had to bring their honey, cheese, butter, eggs, meat and so on to the town's tradesmen who would determine the price of their goods."

"And I bet that it was the lowest price possible!" said Dad.

"Naturally," said the beekeeper. "Merchants within these towns bought cheaply and sold at a high price. But it's a different story today. This pot of honey is a real bargain!"

"We'll buy some after we've been to the castle," Mam promised.

"I might have sold it all by then! Conwy Honey!"

We make our way through the crowds to the castle entrance, where some French people are chatting excitedly as they show their tickets and walk across the bridge to the outer courtyard. We catch a few phrases from the guide's speech: "... *Monsieur Jacques de Saint Georges ... Français ...*"

"She's talking about the castle's architect," said Mam. "She's naturally very proud that it was a Frenchman who designed this specific castle."

"... *sur la liste du patrimoine mondial* ... UNESCO ..."

"She's pointing out that the castle and town walls are on UNESCO's list of World Heritage Sites," Mam translated.

"This is quite different from the round Norman castles built on flat land," observed Gwen. "It's built on rock, a bit like the Welsh castles?"

"The Welsh had an ancient town on this site," said Dad. "But it was destroyed, and Edward had the abbey, the stone coffin of Llywelyn Fawr and many of the old Welsh treasures moved from here."

"... *deux ans* ..." said the guide.

"I remember that from my French lessons at school!" said Gwen excitedly. "She said two years."

TOURELLE

....

Conwy castle has eight strong towers close together on the rock. If we look closely we can see that four thin towers rise above four of these towers. These upper towers are known by the French name *tourelle*, and they're part of the architect's defensive tricks.

Conwy town walls have 21 towers. This is one of the strongest sites built by Edward I – and certainly the costliest. Yet in 1401, it fell to Gwilym and Rhys Tudur, who claimed the castle in the name of their prince, Owain Glyndŵr. The system of castles was ineffective against the national revolt of Glyndŵr and most of them were left to deteriorate after that time.

"Yes, it was all built between 1283 and 1285," explained Dad. "Edward was in a great hurry because he still feared the Welsh." We'd reached the furthest part of the castle, where the grandest and most secure rooms of the king and queen were situated.

"… *les chambres du roi et la reine* …"

"Conwy Honey!" Luckily, the stallholder still has honey for sale as we cross the square again.

"What did you see in the castle then?" he asked as he gave us change for two jars.

"The queen's chamber," said Gwen.

"Oh, each beehive has a queen's chamber too. Have you heard the story about honey and this castle? In 1294, the Welsh were fed up of the rule of the castles – the heavy taxes, the unjust laws. Madog ap Llywelyn sarted a rebellion in Gwynedd. Edward and his large army were surrounded in the castle, with the Welsh bowmen on the high ground all around. No one could enter or leave the castle safely. The weather was too stormy for ships to bring in provisions from Chester. The entire army, including Edward were starving and on the verge of surrendering to the Welsh. They were kept alive by two things, water from the well and honey. Conwy Honey!"

Followers 873

Gruff's mate Draig
The Red Dragon is still higher than all the towers!

Gwen's mate Gwcw
No Welsh people within the town walls! Edward was an old racist king.

Grandma
Honey through the winter – aren't you lucky children?

In the spacious inner courtyard at Caernarfon castle, an actor is performing a 'Character from History' show. He wears a collarless shirt and a quarryman's cap, but he also has a pair of wide green trousers, and a bow and quiver of arrows over his shoulder. He is barefoot. We join groups of local schoolchildren who are here to watch – and to take part – in the performance.

"Welcome to Caernarfon castle!" this character proclaims. "This is a one-man drama – except that you have a part to play as well. Look around you. This is one of the most splendid castles in the world. It's a theatre of a castle. It's a film set of a castle, and the film tells us a story. This giant castle, with its foundations in the two rivers, Menai and Seiont, has high towers threatening the peaks of Eryri in the distance. This is one of the most legendary and historic sites of the Welsh people, and the Normans tried to occupy this land for over two hundred years. Follow me!"

We follow him to the upper part of the courtyard where a slate circle in the grass forms a stage.

"I am Madog, one of the Welshmen watching an army of workers building the walls and towers, and creating a harbour on the banks of the Menai to bring in stones from quarries in England. I was also a quarryman in Dinorwig when slates came by train from Llanberis to Y Felinheli to be shipped to cities all over the world."

The actor makes all of us soldiers in Madog ap Llywelyn's army. Madog had lost much of his family's land to the Normans and he had tried to appeal for the return of the land in one of the Norman lawcourts, but the answer of the Anglesey High Sheriff was "No!" We've become part of Madog's army crossing from Anglesey to Caernarfon in 1294 to teach the High Sheriff a lesson.

"The workmen have finished building the harbour and towers facing the Menai Strait," said the actor playing Madog. "But there's a break in the walls on the other side, and that is where we will be able to enter the town and castle, burn the buildings and occupy the site for six months."

THE EAGLE TOWER

....

Wales' most famous tower, the Eagle Tower, with three strong turrets on top, stands above the meeting place of the Menai and Seiont. Flagpoles are placed on two of those turrets. Those flagpoles carry two Red Dragons today.

The name of the tower is interesting. Eagles were common in Wales in those days. The word *eryr* means 'a high bird' (and Eryri, sometimes called Snowdonia, means 'high mountains'). The eagle is considered the king of birds, and there were three eagles on the shield of Owain Gwynedd, one of the most important Welsh princes.

This is certainly a dramatic castle – stone carvings of eagles can still be seen on top of the Eagle Tower today.

But there was real drama here in 1932. Welshmen had requested that the Red Dragon be hoisted on the Eagle Tower on St. David's Day. 'No!' said the High Sheriff. A group of young people climbed to the top of the Eagle Tower, removed the old flag, and raised the Red Dragon. It has flown there ever since.

For several minutes we shout and hurl imaginary burning torches in the castle's inner ward. Then Madog silences us by raising his arm.

"Unfortunately, stones don't burn. After Madog's rebellion, the building work continued. The Normans spent forty years building this castle – the theatrical castle had to be perfect."

He leads us to the Queen's Tower.

"Eleanor of Castile, Edward's wife, stayed here in 1284, although this tower hadn't been completed at that date. Her second son – Edward – was born here in Caernarfon and tradition states that he was called the 'Prince of Wales'. So the title 'Prince of Wales' was carried from this country, over the river Severn, to London."

We're back at the slate circle.

"Now we're all quarrymen. I want you to pretend to carry huge slate slabs from the quarry into the castle. There you go, six men to each slab. Put them down here. Why? Well, we're now in 1969, and the quarrymen are preparing the stage to bring the title 'Prince of Wales' back across the river Severn to Caernarfon temporarily. But . . . "

We're all hushed as we watch Madog remove his cap and hurl it to the ground.

"... They promised a new age for Wales. The world will come to Caernarfon. Visitors! Wealth! But what really happened? When the title returned over the Severn, they shut the quarry and 350 quarrymen, including Madog, lost their jobs."

Followers 936

Gwen's mate Angel
The eagles on the Eagle Tower have done a good job!

Gruff's mate Gwil
Stealing Welsh land! Stealing a Welsh title! The same old story ...

Gramps
We've been to the Welsh Slate Museum at Llanberis – at one time it was the largest slate quarry in the world, employing over 3,000 workers.

"Look at this view of the castle from the air," said Dad. "The design is so perfect, it could have been built out of Lego."

We are visiting the last great castle built by Edward in Wales. This is probably the most perfect, as the architect, James of St George, was allowed to choose his site and clear the land in order to build his masterpiece. It's a circle within a circle – a ring of outer moats, a box of walls and turrets with a high wall and tall towers within that box and, finally, a strong fortress in the centre.

"Building this castle almost ruined Edward financially, making his reign bankrupt," said the lady taking our order in a cafe on the street nearby. "In today's money, Edward spent around £40 million on the castles he built in Wales – the most expensive building project in the whole of Europe during the Middle Ages. Each battle cost him money as he bought ships and seamen from the southern ports of England, soldiers with crossbows from Gascony, mounted soldiers from English castles, and, at one time, over 15 thousand foot soldiers from all parts of Europe. Madog's rebellion had cost Edward about £30 million in today's money – showing how determined he was to rule our country."

Before long, she returns with a large pot of tea and a plate of Welsh cakes.

"Here you are, your Welsh tea!" she smiled. But she had another story to tell us also. "Madog's revolt had scared the Normans – they never thought the Welsh would fight back. So, despite the cost, they were forced to build Beaumaris castle so that they had a strong military presence at each end of the Menai Straits. '*Beau mareys*' the Normans called the spot – beautiful marsh! But there was already a Welsh village here called Cerrig-y-gwyddyl, and Llanfaes nearby had a Welsh harbour. Both were destroyed and the native people driven from this fertile land to the sand dunes of Newborough."

She moves on to wait on a nearby table.

"Can you imagine how those Welsh people felt?" said Gwen. "Having to leave their homes and farms – and being forced to live on sand dunes."

WATER

....

The strongest castle is useless without water. Since the defensive plans of the Normans often included deep ditches, these were filled with tidal water in those castles which were built on the coast.

But fresh drinking water was also vital. If the castle was laid to siege by an attacking army, a freshwater well within the castle walls was essential. Sometimes – as in Conwy castle, for example – the deep shaft of the well had to be dug out of bare rock to reach the water. Since Beaumaris castle was built on marshland, water was plentiful here!

On her way back with the order for the other table, the lady at the teashop added:

"But Owain Glyndŵr got the better of them, despite their grand castles and perfect plans! He burnt down their township and took over the castle for two years."

She smiles as she goes back to the kitchen, before appearing with another pot of tea.

Mam says, "Thanks. It's great to get the history from the viewpoint of a local. Do you live in Beaumaris?"

"No," she says. "I'm from Newborough."

Followers 987

Griff's mate Bîns
I fancy that Welsh tea!

Gwen's mate Nervous Nerys
Moving the Welsh out to make room for the castle! How awful!

Grandad
We saw a place called Llys Llywelyn at St Fagans National Museum of History. It's a copy of one of the old buildings found at Newborough.

The school eisteddfod is approaching and we have brought the script we've prepared to one of the castles in the Vale of Glamorgan for a rehearsal.

Imagine the scene. Summer 1401. Glyndŵr's army is attacking the Normans in all corners of Wales. One day the floodwaters of the river Dee help him to beat his enemy. Then he makes use of the steep hillside and the setting sun to beat a large army on Pumlumon. In a short while, he's at Abergavenny. The Normans throughout Wales are on edge. This is true of Sir Laurence Berkerolles, constable of Coity castle – which had recently been restored. Sir Laurence is very proud of his castle. Gruff is playing his part here.

Sir Laurence: Oh, what am I to do? I'm here on top of my beloved castle's tower. But all day, every day I have to dash to the *garderobe*. I've got butterflies in my tummy, and I've no control of my insides. I'm scared stiff that the army of that rogue, Owain Glyndŵr, is in the hills and about to descend like a pack of hounds to wreck my lovely castle. Oh no! Two horsemen are riding up to the gatehouse. Who on earth are they? Hey! Watchman! Address them through the arrow slit. I want to know their names and what business they have here. Oh dear! I have some business to attend to as well …

By the time Gruff came back on stage he'd received the information from the Watchman.

Sir Laurence: What? They speak French? They're two respectable Normans? Well, open the gate! Welcome them. Perhaps they have news of that beastly Owain. Ah! *Bienvenu, mes amis.* Welcome friends. The grooms will take care of your horses. Join me in my lavish hall for a cup of wine after your tiring journey.

I'm acting Owain Glyndŵr and I must remember to speak with a French accent.

Owain Glyndŵr: *Merçi.* The hospitality of Sir Laurence Berkerolles is well-known in Wales and as far as France. It's a pleasure to meet you, sir.

Sir Laurence: Tut, tut! We Normans have to stick together in these dark days. See any trouble on your way? Any sign of Owain …

Owain: We saw three castles and three townships burnt to the ground between here and Shrewsbury, my friend.

Sir Laurence: Oh! *Sacre bleu*, goodness me. Excuse me – I have to visit the *garderobe* …

Owain: Well, Rhys. We're inside the castle. Keep a look out and count how many soldiers there are. This part of the castle is very grand. Shh, here he comes.

GARDEROBES

....

Even though old castles look enormous, they could seem very small if there was an army of a thousand soldiers and their servants there from time to time. One practical problem this caused was simply: 'Where's the loo?' Just think of a hundred horses in one of the courtyards – the smell of horse manure would be pretty strong. So where were the toilets in a large castle?

Well, there's an interesting row of them on one section of the outer walls of Conwy town. They were designed to be outside the castle, with all the waste dropped outside the town walls. A bit like a row of swallows' nests …

But of course, the high and mighty were not expected to go along the outer walls to answer the call of nature. Private chambers were sometimes built within the thickness of the walls – there's a good example at Dolwyddelan castle.

At Manorbier and Coity, there are specific towers built for the important loos. The Norman word for these was *garderobes* – clothing and personal treasures were kept there also. This is an early version of 'wardrobe'.

Sir Laurence: Are you in a hurry, my friends? Not many Normans travel any distance these days. You're very brave. Why don't you rest here for a few days and tell me all the latest news?

Some music is played at this point to show that time has passed.

Sir Laurence: Do you have to go already? I've only had three days and nights of your excellent company.

Owain: Duty calls, I'm afraid. We have important tasks ahead.

Sir Laurence: Of course, of course. Two clever gentlemen such as yourselves must have many duties. Well, *au revoir*. Goodbye. Keep away from the clutches of those barbaric Welshmen.

Owain: Oh, don't worry. We'll be heading for the Normans hereabout.

Sir Laurence: I've just realised that I don't know your names. Before you go, please tell me, so that I can praise you to all my friends in the area.

Owain: I, Owain Glyndŵr and my general, Rhys Gethin, shake you by the hand and thank you for your generous hospitality ...

Sir Laurence: The *garderobe*! Out of my way! I've got to go to the *garderobe* ...

Followers 1065

Gwen's mate Catrin
I'm looking forward to hearing your French accents.

Gruff's mate Tracs
A hole in the outer wall – very, very high up? No thanks!

Gran
A good script! Nothing beats a bit of character acting to bring history alive.

As we walk into the castle at Harlech, there's the sound of gunshot from the woods above the town. "Maybe someone is shooting crows?" says Dad. "It's the lambing season, and lots of farmers are losing lambs to crows. The people of this town are nicknamed 'Harlech Crows' – it seems that many crows nested in the ruins of this castle when it was abandoned."

"Perhaps the shooting you hear is an echo of the battles of the past," interrupts a deep voice from the shadows of the gatehouse. A bearded man dressed in black leather comes out into the light.

"Can you hear it? That's gunpowder," he adds. "That sound was heard in this castle over six hundred years ago. It's a sound representing the end of an era for the castles. Why don't you come in and see the splendour of the place?"

He leads us into the inner courtyard, then up some stairs to the top of the walls. The view is amazing – the mountains of Eryri as a backdrop, the long arm of Llŷn in the west, and the blue sea of Cardigan Bay in front of us.

"Isn't this a perfect spot to build a castle?" asks the man in black leather. "The most important era in this castle's history was 1404–1410 when Owain Glyndŵr raided the place and made it the centre of his new Wales. He held a parliament here in 1405. Delegates from Spain, Scotland and France were welcomed here and the whole of Wales was ruled by Glyndŵr at that time. Think of the excitement here! So much power, so much splendour. The roots of modern Wales were planted on this very spot."

From the parapets, we can see the 108 carefully protected steps which lead down from the castle to the bottom of the rough crag upon which the castle stands. This is the route down to the sea. "But the sea is miles from the base of the crag," exclaimed Gwen.

"Yes, by now," replies the man in black. "But in olden days those sand dunes didn't exist. The seashore was where the railway lies now. Ships could sail right up to the rock. And that was Owain Glyndŵr's escape route in the end."

"Escape?" says Gwen. "And leave this strong headquarters?"

DWELLING

A castle was primarily a military structure, but it often had to provide a home for high-ranking officials and their families. Inside the strong defences – the thick, bare walls and all the ingenious architectural features to safeguard the site – there had to be a fairly grand and comfortable living space, which was also totally secure.

Some claim that the oldest, grandest 'palace' in the whole of Wales was at Harlech castle. It faces west, so the setting sun would have been reflected in its fine windows. Its stylish grace was more like that of a nobleman's country residence than a refuge within a castle. James of St George – the architect of Edward's castles – made this his home after completing the project. He was Harlech castle's first constable.

This is also where Owain Glyndŵr and his family came at the height of his national rebellion. He had a grand court at Sycharth and another at Glyndyfrdwy but both were attacked and burnt by the army of the English king's son in 1403. In the spring of 1404, Harlech castle fell to Glyndŵr's army after a long siege. The castle provided the leader with a sumptuous dwelling for his wife and children and their families for the following six years.

"Yes. The sound of gunpowder. That's what frightened the Welsh who were here in the castle. The king's army had brought a huge cannon to Harlech, and for over a year it had been firing stone missiles at the castle. Imagine the noise. Think of the havoc as the missiles destroyed the walls or landed on buildings in the courtyard."

"I didn't know that gunpowder was used during Glyndŵr's rebellion," says Gwen.

"Cannons had been used on both sides during the Hundred Years War in France. It's quite possible that Glyndŵr had paid for big guns to accompany the 3,000 Frenchmen who came to support his cause. The cannons were used to greatest effect here in Harlech and in Aberystwyth. A huge 5,000 pound cannon called the 'Messenger' was used by the English king's army to fire against Aberystwyth castle in 1407 and the Welsh yielded the castle in 1408. From 1408 onwards, another massive cannon named 'The King's Daughter' fired missiles against Glyndŵr's headquarters here at Harlech."

"So he had to escape by sea?" asks Gwen.

"It was impossible to defend the castle. Gunpowder put an end to the age of the castles. Owain had to flee with a handful of his most loyal soldiers. They went by boat down the coast to a place still called Owain Glyndŵr's Cave."

"And his wife and children?" asks Gwen.

"They were captured and imprisoned in the Tower of London. But while Glyndŵr was still at large hidden in his cave, there was still hope for Wales. No one betrayed him."

Followers 1155

Gruff's mate Draig
Owain Glyndŵr's Cave – I'd love to see that!

Gwen's mate Gwcw
Gunpowder – it still creates havoc and separates families to this day.

Grandad
I hadn't heard that story about Owain Glyndŵr before. There's such a lot of history associated with him!

We have just returned from Pembroke castle, where we had a brilliant guided tour. This was what our guide said:

"Good morning. My name is Rhys and I'm your guide today. We're in south-west Wales, on a headland where Pembroke town and castle stand on the banks of the river Cleddau. The Welsh name 'Penfro' says it all – *pen y fro* means the far end of the land. Beyond Pembroke we must travel to foreign lands.

"That's exactly what happened to Harri Tudur (Henry Tudor) in 1471. He was 14 years' old at the time. His grandfather, Owain Tudur, had married the English king's widow. She was a Frenchwoman called Catherine of Valois. Many people at court in London objected to this marriage. Since the days of Edward I and of Glyndŵr's rebellion, many laws were passed to punish the Welsh – the Welsh Penal Laws. During the Middle Ages the Welsh were the worst treated nation in Europe – no Welshman could own land or hold office in any town in Wales or the Marches; they could not bear arms or defend their homes or gather in a large crowd without permission. They could not govern laws or pass judgement against Englishmen – and if an Englishman married a Welshwoman, he lost all his rights as an Englishman. Even though Catherine of Valois was French, Owain Tudur was accused of marrying an Englishwoman without permission, among other things. In the end poor Owain was beheaded in the town square at Hereford.

"This was during a time of great trouble and fighting between the Normans in England and France. Between 1350–1450, the Hundred Years War, as it came to be known, was fought in France. Then, between 1455–1485, the battles took place in England and the Marches – this was the War of the Roses. By the end, the noble Norman families had almost killed each other off completely.

"What has all that to do with a castle at the far reaches of Wales? Well, in 1457 Harri Tudur was born here. Since his grandfather had married the English king's widow, and so many of the family had been killed in the wars, he had a strong claim on the English throne. Many people

BANNER

'Showing your colours' was vital in a castle and in battle. Each prince and each leader had his own coat of arms – Owain Gwynedd's coat of arms had three eagles, Llywelyn Fawr had four standing lions and Owain Glyndŵr had four lions rampant.

The Red Dragon is the oldest flag of all the world's countries, using a symbol which dates back to Roman times. In those days, each section of an army carried the symbol of a dragon at the head, and the soldier in charge was called a *draconarius*. In the Welsh language, the word *draig* (dragon) came to mean 'the soldier at the head of the army' and it can be found in the name of King Arthur's father: Uthr Bendragon.

The last of the Welsh kings to rule the whole of south Britain was Cadwaladr ap Cadwallon, who reigned until 688. His coat of arms was also the Red Dragon and several legends describe the red dragon (Wales) fighting the white dragon (England). Glyndŵr's army flew a golden dragon during their campaigns. But the dragon was more than just a coat of arms for one leader – it was a banner for an entire nation.

When Harri Tudur marched through Wales on his journey from Pembroke to Bosworth, he united the Red Dragon with the traditional colours worn by Welshmen in battle – green and white. Those are, of course, the colours of the leek – another national symbol of Wales.

The Red Dragon was on the Mimosa on the voyage to Patagonia. It has travelled the world with male voice choirs and can be seen on the kit of the Welsh women's football team. The old, old Red Dragon still flies proudly and prominently.

threatened his life as a result and in 1471, his uncle, Jasper, took him by ship from Pembroke to St Malo in Brittany. He found sanctuary there for 14 years. By 1485, Richard III was the unpopular king on the throne in London, with rather a lot of blood on his hands, so it seems.

"Harri and Jasper considered it the right time to return to Wales. Plenty of people in Normandy and Brittany were willing to support them and on August 7th 1485 an army of 3,000 landed in south Pembrokeshire. This army had a huge red, green and white banner flying at its head. William Brandon was the man carrying the Red Dragon, and the banner inspired the Welsh to fight. The army marched at a cracking pace from Pembroke to Machynlleth, covering some 20 miles a day.

"The news spread like wildfire. The Welsh from the north, the south west, the south east and mid-Wales were rallied. Jasper and Harri turned east at Machynlleth and before crossing the border at Shrewsbury, almost the whole of Wales were united under the Red Dragon.

"On 22 August 7,000 of Harri Tudur's soldiers came face to face with over 10,000 of Richard III's men at Bosworth field in the English Midlands. Richard saw that the Red Dragon flew above a particular regiment, so he sent his cavalry to attack that regiment directly. He knew that Harri (Henry Tudor) would not be far from that banner. The bearer of the flag, William Brandon, was killed. But I, Rhys ap Maredudd from Plas Iolyn, Pentrefoelas stood next to him. I raised the Red Dragon high. At that very moment, the Stanleys and their ranks from north-east Wales reached the field of battle. Once again the whole of Wales followed the Red Dragon. Richard III was killed and our man was crowned Henry VII. But in our minds, it was the Red Dragon that won the day for us."

Followers 1268

Gwen's mate Angel
Can you catch a ferry from Pembroke to St Malo today? It would be a wonderful trip.

Gruff's mate Gwil
Welsh Penal Laws – what a way to treat people in their own country!

Gran
And so the old Red Dragon I took to the Arms Park has had a taste of twenty Welsh castles! Thank you so much, Gwen and Gruff.

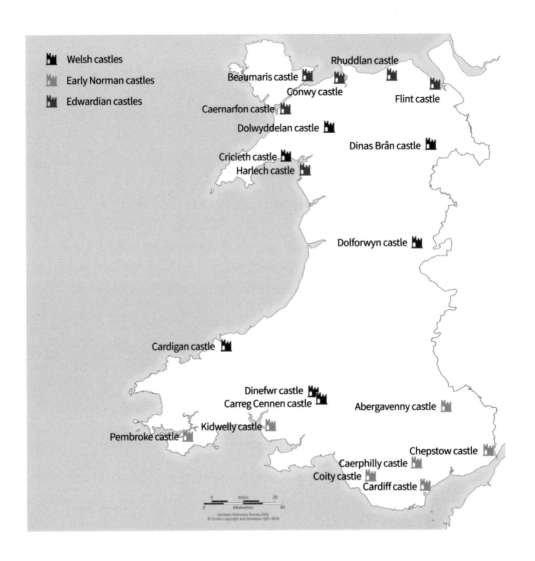

Welsh castles

Early Norman castles

Edwardian castles

Beaumaris castle
Rhuddlan castle
Conwy castle
Flint castle
Caernarfon castle
Dolwyddelan castle
Dinas Brân castle
Cricieth castle
Harlech castle
Dolforwyn castle
Cardigan castle
Dinefwr castle
Carreg Cennen castle
Abergavenny castle
Kidwelly castle
Pembroke castle
Chepstow castle
Caerphilly castle
Coity castle
Cardiff castle

0   miles   20
0   kilometres   40

Contains Ordnance Survey data
© Crown copyright and database right 2018